DASH DIE
COOKBOO

The Best Guide to Lower yo
Pressure with Quick and Easy
Recipes.

Live Healthy with Low Sodiui
Tasty Dishes.

Sandra Podolski

Table of Contents

The information in the following pages is broadly considered a truthful and accurate account of facts and as such, any inattention, use, or misuse of the information in question by the reader will render any resulting actions solely under their purview. There are no scenarios in which the publisher or the original author of this work can be in any fashion deemed liable for any hardship or damages that may befall them after undertaking information described herein.

Additionally, the information in the following pages is intended only for informational purposes and should thus be thought of as universal. As befitting its nature, it is presented without assurance regarding its prolonged validity or interim quality. Trademarks that are mentioned are done without written consent and can in no way be considered an endorsement from the trademark holder.

Breakfast

Blueberry Waffles

Preparation time: 15 minutes

Cooking time: 15 minutes

Servings: 8

Ingredients:

- 2 cups whole wheat flour

- 1 tablespoon baking powder

- 1 teaspoon ground cinnamon

- 2 tablespoons sugar

- 2 large eggs

- 3 tablespoons unsalted butter, melted

- 3 tablespoons nonfat plain Greek yogurt

- 1½ cups 1% milk

- 2 teaspoons vanilla extract

- 4 ounces blueberries

- Nonstick cooking spray

- ½ cup maple almond butter

Directions:

1. Preheat waffle iron. Mix the flour, baking powder, cinnamon, plus sugar in a large bowl. Mix the eggs, melted butter, yogurt, milk, and vanilla in a small bowl. Combine well.

2. Put the wet fixing to the dry mix and whisk until well combined. Do not over whisk; it's okay if the mixture has some lumps. Fold in the blueberries.

3. Oiled the waffle iron with cooking spray, then cook 1/3 cup of the batter until the waffles are lightly browned and slightly crisp. Repeat with the rest of the batter.

4. Place 2 waffles in each of 4 storage containers. Store the almond butter in 4 condiment cups. To serve, top each warm waffle with 1 tablespoon of maple almond butter.

Nutrition:

Calories: 647

Fat: 37g

Carbohydrates: 67g

Protein: 22g

Sodium: 156mg

Apple Pancakes

Preparation time: 15 minutes

Cooking time: 5 minutes

Servings: 16

Ingredients:

- ¼ cup extra-virgin olive oil, divided

- 1 cup whole wheat flour

- 2 teaspoons baking powder

- 1 teaspoon baking soda

- 1 teaspoon ground cinnamon

- 1 cup 1% milk

- 2 large eggs

- 1 medium Gala apple, diced

- 2 tablespoons maple syrup

- ¼ cup chopped walnuts

Directions:

1. Set aside 1 teaspoon of oil to use for greasing a griddle or skillet. In a large bowl, stir the flour, baking powder, baking soda, cinnamon, milk, eggs, apple, and the remaining oil.

2. Warm griddle or skillet on medium-high heat and coat with the reserved oil. Working in batches, pour in about ¼ cup of the batter for each pancake. Cook until browned on both sides.

3. Place 4 pancakes into each of 4 medium storage containers and the maple syrup in 4 small containers. Put each serving with 1 tablespoon of walnuts and drizzle with ½ tablespoon of maple syrup.

Nutrition:

Calories: 378

Fat: 22g

Carbohydrates: 39g

Protein: 10g

Sodium: 65mg

Super-Simple Granola

Preparation time: 15 minutes

Cooking time: 25 minutes

Servings: 8

Ingredients:

- ¼ cup extra-virgin olive oil

- ¼ cup honey

- ½ teaspoon ground cinnamon

- ½ teaspoon vanilla extract

- ¼ teaspoon salt

- 2 cups rolled oats

- ½ cup chopped walnuts

- ½ cup slivered almonds

Directions:

1. Preheat the oven to 350°F. Mix the oil, honey, cinnamon, vanilla, and salt in a large bowl. Add the oats, walnuts, and almonds. Stir to coat. Put the batter out onto the prepared sheet pan. Bake for 20 minutes. Let cool.

Nutrition:

Calories: 254

Fat: 16g

Carbohydrates: 25g

Fiber: 3.5g

Protein: 5g

Potassium: 163mg

Sodium: 73mg

Savory Yogurt Bowls

Preparation time: 15 minutes

Cooking time: 0 minutes

Servings:4

Ingredients:

- 1 medium cucumber, diced

- ½ cup pitted Kalamata olives, halved

- 2 tablespoons fresh lemon juice

- 1 tablespoon extra-virgin olive oil

- 1 teaspoon dried oregano

- ¼ teaspoon freshly ground black pepper

- 2 cups nonfat plain Greek yogurt

- ½ cup slivered almonds

Directions:

1. In a small bowl, mix the cucumber, olives, lemon juice, oil, oregano, and pepper. Divide the yogurt evenly among 4 storage containers. Top with the cucumber-olive mix and almonds.

Nutrition:

Calories: 240

Fat: 16g

Carbohydrates: 10g

Protein: 16g

Potassium: 353mg

Sodium: 350mg

Energy Sunrise Muffins

Preparation time: 15 minutes

Cooking time: 25 minutes

Servings: 16

Ingredients:

- Nonstick cooking spray

- 2 cups whole wheat flour

- 2 teaspoons baking soda

- 2 teaspoons ground cinnamon

- 1 teaspoon ground ginger

- ¼ teaspoon salt

- 3 large eggs

- ½ cup packed brown sugar

- 1/3 cup unsweetened applesauce

- ¼ cup honey

- ¼ cup vegetable or canola oil

- 1 teaspoon grated orange zest

- Juice of 1 medium orange

- 2 teaspoons vanilla extract

- 2 cups shredded carrots

- 1 large apple, peeled and grated

- ½ cup golden raisins

- ½ cup chopped pecans

- ½ cup unsweetened coconut flakes

Directions:

1. If you can fit two 12-cup muffin tins side by side in your oven, then leave a rack in the middle, then preheat the oven to 350°F.

2. Coat 16 cups of the muffin tins with cooking spray or line with paper liners. Mix the flour, baking soda, cinnamon, ginger, and salt in a large bowl. Set aside.

3. Mix the eggs, brown sugar, applesauce, honey, oil, orange zest, orange juice, and vanilla until combined in a medium bowl. Add the carrots and apple and whisk again.

4. Mix the dry and wet ingredients with a spatula. Fold in the raisins, pecans, and coconut. Mix everything once again, just until well combined. Put the batter into the prepared muffin cups, filling them to the top.

5. Bake within 20 to 25 minutes, or until a wooden toothpick inserted into the middle of the center muffin comes out clean (switching racks halfway through if baking on 2 racks). Cool for 5 minutes in the tins, then transfers to a wire rack to cool for an additional 5 minutes. Cool completely before storing in containers.

Nutrition:

Calories: 292

Fat: 14g

Carbohydrates: 42g

Protein: 5g

Sodium: 84mg

Spinach, Egg, And Cheese Breakfast Quesadillas

Preparation time: 15 minutes

Cooking time: 15 minutes

Servings: 4

Ingredients:

- 1½ tablespoons extra-virgin olive oil

- ½ medium onion, diced

- 1 medium red bell pepper, diced

- 4 large eggs

- 1/8 teaspoon salt

- 1/8 teaspoon freshly ground black pepper

- 4 cups baby spinach

- ½ cup crumbled feta cheese

- Nonstick cooking spray

- 4 (6-inch) whole-wheat tortillas, divided

- 1 cup shredded part-skim low-moisture mozzarella cheese, divided

Directions:

Warm-up oil over medium heat in a large skillet. Add the onion and bell pepper and sauté for about 5 minutes, or until soft.

1. Mix the eggs, salt, and black pepper in a medium bowl. Stir in the spinach and feta cheese. Put the egg batter in the skillet and scramble for about 2 minutes, or until the eggs are cooked. Remove from the heat.

2. Coat a clean skillet with cooking spray and add 2 tortillas. Place one-quarter of the spinach-egg mixture on one side of each tortilla. Sprinkle each with ¼ cup of mozzarella cheese. Fold the other halves of the tortillas down to close the quesadillas and brown for about 1 minute.

3. Turnover and cook again in a minute on the other side. Repeat with the remaining 2 tortillas and ½ cup of mozzarella cheese. Cut each quesadilla in half or wedges. Divide among 4 storage containers or reusable bags.

Nutrition:

Calories: 453

Fat: 28g

Carbohydrates: 28g

Fiber: 4.5g

Protein: 23g

Potassium: 205mg

Sodium: 837mg

Simple Cheese and Broccoli Omelets

Preparation time: 15 minutes

Cooking time: 10 minutes

Servings: 4

Ingredients:

- 3 tablespoons extra-virgin olive oil, divided

- 2 cups chopped broccoli

- 8 large eggs

- ¼ cup 1% milk

- ½ teaspoon freshly ground black pepper

- 8 tablespoons shredded reduced-fat Monterey Jack cheese, divided

Directions:

1. In a nonstick skillet, heat 1 tablespoon of oil over medium-high heat. Add the broccoli and sauté, occasionally stirring, for 3 to 5 minutes, or until the broccoli turns bright green. Scrape into a bowl.

2. Mix the eggs, milk, plus pepper in a small bowl. Wipe out the skillet and heat ½ tablespoon of oil. Add one-quarter of the egg mixture and tilt the skillet to ensure an even layer. Cook for 2 minutes and then add 2 tablespoons of cheese and one-

quarter of the broccoli. Use a spatula to fold into an omelet.

3. Repeat step 3 with the remaining 1½ tablespoons of oil, remaining egg mixture, 6 tablespoons of cheese, and remaining broccoli to make a total of 4 omelets. Divide into 4 storage containers.

Nutrition:

Calories: 292

Fat: 23g

Carbohydrates: 4g

Fiber: 1g

Protein: 18g

Potassium: 308mg

Sodium: 282mg

Creamy Avocado and Egg Salad Sandwiches

Preparation time: 15 minutes

Cooking time: 15 minutes

Servings: 4

Ingredients:

- 2 small avocados, halved and pitted

- 2 tablespoons nonfat plain Greek yogurt

- Juice of 1 large lemon

- ¼ teaspoon salt

- ½ teaspoon freshly ground black pepper

- 8 large eggs, hardboiled, peeled, and chopped

- 3 tablespoons finely chopped fresh dill

- 3 tablespoons finely chopped fresh parsley

- 8 whole wheat bread slices (or your choice)

Directions:

1. Scoop the avocados into a large bowl and mash. Mix in the yogurt, lemon juice, salt, and pepper. Add the eggs, dill, and parsley and combine.

2. Store the bread and salad separately in 4 reusable storage bags and 4 containers and assemble the

night before or serving. To serve, divide the mixture evenly among 4 of the bread slices and top with the other slices to make sandwiches.

Nutrition:

Calories: 488

Fat: 22g

Carbohydrates: 48g

Fiber: 8g

Protein: 23g

Potassium: 469mg

Sodium: 597mg

Breakfast Hash

Preparation time: 15 minutes

Cooking time: 25 minutes

Servings: 4

Ingredients:

- Nonstick cooking spray

- 2 large sweet potatoes, ½-inch cubes

- 1 scallion, finely chopped

- ¼ teaspoon salt

- ½ teaspoon freshly ground black pepper

- 8 ounces extra-lean ground beef (96% or leaner)

- 1 medium onion, diced

- 2 garlic cloves, minced

- 1 red bell pepper, diced

- ¼ teaspoon ground cumin

- ¼ teaspoon paprika

- 2 cups coarsely chopped kale leaves

- ¾ cup shredded reduced-fat Cheddar cheese

- 4 large eggs

Directions:

1. Oiled a large skillet with cooking spray and heat over medium heat. Add the sweet potatoes, scallion, salt, and pepper. Sauté for 10 minutes, stirring often.

2. Add the beef, onion, garlic, bell pepper, cumin, and paprika. Sauté, frequently stirring, for about 4 minutes, or until the meat browns. Add the kale to the skillet and stir until wilted. Sprinkle with the Cheddar cheese.

3. Make four wells in the hash batter and crack an egg into each. Cover and let the eggs cook until the white is fully cooked and the yolk is to your liking. Divide into 4 storage containers.

Nutrition:

Calories: 323

Fat: 15g

Carbohydrates: 23g

Fiber: 4g

Protein: 25g

Potassium: 676mg

Sodium: 587mg

Hearty Breakfast Casserole

Preparation time: 15 minutes

Cooking time: 30 minutes

Servings: 4

Ingredients:

- Nonstick cooking spray

- 1 large green bell pepper, diced

- 8 ounces cremini mushrooms, diced

- ½ medium onion, diced

- 3 garlic cloves, minced

- 1 large sweet potato, grated

- 1 cup baby spinach

- 12 large eggs

- 3 tablespoons 1% milk

- 1 teaspoon mustard powder

- 1 teaspoon paprika

- 1 teaspoon freshly ground black pepper

- ½ teaspoon salt

- ½ cup shredded reduced-fat Colby-Jack cheese

Directions:

1. Preheat the oven to 350°F. Oiled at a 9-by-13-inch baking dish with cooking spray. Coat a large skillet with cooking spray and heat over medium heat. Add the bell pepper, mushrooms, onion, garlic, and sweet potato.

2. Sauté, frequently stirring, for 3 to 4 minutes, or until the onion is translucent. Add the spinach and continue to sauté while stirring, until the spinach has wilted. Remove, then set aside to cool slightly.

3. Mix the eggs, milk, mustard powder, paprika, black pepper, and salt in a large bowl. Add the sautéed vegetables. Put the batter into the prepared baking dish.

4. Bake for 30 minutes. Remove from the oven, sprinkle with the Colby-Jack cheese, return to the oven, and bake again within 5 minutes to melt the cheese. Divide into 4 storage containers.

Nutrition:

Calories: 378

Fat: 25g

Carbohydrates: 17g

Fiber: 3g

Protein: 26g

Potassium: 717mg

Sodium: 658mg

Creamy Apple-Avocado Smoothie

Preparation time: 15 minutes

Cooking time: 0 minutes

Servings: 2

Ingredients:

- ½ medium avocado, peeled and pitted

- 1 medium apple, chopped

- 1 cup baby spinach leaves

- 1 cup nonfat vanilla Greek yogurt

- ½ to 1 cup of water

- 1 cup ice

- Freshly squeezed lemon juice (optional)

Directions:

1. Blend all of the fixing using a blender, and blend until smooth and creamy. Put a squeeze of lemon juice on top if desired, and serve immediately.

Nutrition:

Calories: 200

Fat: 7g

Sodium: 56mg

Potassium: 378mg

Carbohydrates: 27g

Fiber: 5g

Sugars: 20g

Protein: 10g

Strawberry, Orange, and Beet Smoothie

Preparation time: 5 minutes

Cooking time: 0 minutes

Servings: 2

Ingredients:

- 1 cup nonfat milk

- 1 cup of frozen strawberries

- 1 medium beet, cooked, peeled, and cubed

- 1 orange, peeled and quartered

- 1 frozen banana, peeled and chopped

- 1 cup nonfat vanilla Greek yogurt

- 1 cup ice

Directions:

1. In a blender, combine all of the fixings, and blend until smooth. Serve immediately.

Nutrition:

Calories: 266

Fat: 0g

Cholesterol: 7mg

Sodium: 104mg

Carbohydrates: 51g

Fiber: 6g

Sugars: 34g

Protein: 15g

Blueberry-Vanilla Yogurt Smoothie

Preparation time: 5 minutes

Cooking time: 0 minutes

Servings: 2

Ingredients:

- 1½ cups frozen blueberries

- 1 cup nonfat vanilla Greek yogurt

- 1 frozen banana, peeled and sliced

- ½ cup nonfat or low-fat milk

- 1 cup ice

Directions:

1. In a blender, combine all of the fixing listed, and blend until smooth and creamy. Serve immediately.

Nutrition:

Calories: 228

Fat: 1g

Sodium: 63mg

Potassium: 470mg

Carbohydrates: 45g

Fiber: 5g

Sugars: 34g

Protein: 12g

Greek Yogurt Oat Pancakes

Preparation time: 15 minutes

Cooking time: 10 minutes

Servings: 2

Ingredients:

- 6 egg whites (or ¾ cup liquid egg whites)

- 1 cup rolled oats

- 1 cup plain nonfat Greek yogurt

- 1 medium banana, peeled and sliced

- 1 teaspoon ground cinnamon

- 1 teaspoon baking powder

Directions:

1. Blend all of the listed fixing using a blender. Warm a griddle over medium heat. Spray the skillet with nonstick cooking spray.

2. Put 1/3 cup of the mixture or batter onto the griddle. Allow to cook and flip when bubbles on the top burst, about 5 minutes. Cook again within a minute until golden brown. Repeat with the remaining batter. Divide between two serving plates and enjoy.

Nutrition:

Calories: 318

Fat: 4g

Sodium: 467mg

Potassium: 634mg

Carbohydrates: 47g

Fiber: 6g

Sugars: 13g

Protein: 28g

Scrambled Egg and Veggie Breakfast Quesadillas

Preparation time: 15 minutes

Cooking time: 15 minutes

Servings: 2

Ingredients:

- 2 eggs

- 2 egg whites

- 2 to 4 tablespoons nonfat or low-fat milk

- ¼ teaspoon freshly ground black pepper

- 1 large tomato, chopped

- 2 tablespoons chopped cilantro

- ½ cup canned black beans, rinsed and drained

- 1½ tablespoons olive oil, divided

- 4 corn tortillas

- ½ avocado, peeled, pitted, and thinly sliced

Directions:

1. Mix the eggs, egg whites, milk, and black pepper in a bowl. Using an electric mixer, beat until smooth. To the same bowl, add the tomato, cilantro, and black beans, and fold into the eggs with a spoon.

2. Warm-up half of the olive oil in a medium pan over medium heat. Add the scrambled egg mixture and cook for a few minutes, stirring, until cooked through. Remove from the pan.

3. Divide the scrambled-egg mixture between the tortillas, layering only on one half of the tortilla. Top with avocado slices and fold the tortillas in half.

4. Heat the remaining oil over medium heat, and add one of the folded tortillas to the pan. Cook within 1 to 2 minutes on each side or until browned. Repeat with remaining tortillas. Serve immediately.

Nutrition:

Calories: 445

Fat: 24g

Sodium: 228mg

Potassium: 614mg

Carbohydrates: 42g

Fiber: 11g

Sugars: 2g

Protein: 19g

Stuffed Breakfast Peppers

Preparation time: 15 minutes

Cooking time: 45 minutes

Servings: 4

Ingredients:

- 4 bell peppers (any color)

- 1 (16-ounce) bag frozen spinach

- 4 eggs

- ¼ cup shredded low-fat cheese (optional)

- Freshly ground black pepper

Directions:

1. Preheat the oven to 400°F. Line a baking dish with aluminum foil. Cut the tops off the pepper, then discard the seeds. Discard the tops and seeds. Put the peppers in the baking dish, and bake for about 15 minutes.

2. While the peppers bake, defrost the spinach and drain off the excess moisture. Remove the peppers, then stuff the bottoms evenly with the defrosted spinach.

3. Crack an egg over the spinach inside each pepper. Top each egg with a tablespoon of the cheese (if

using) and season with black pepper to taste. Bake within 15 to 20 minutes, or until the egg whites are set and opaque.

Nutrition:

Calories: 136

Fat: 5g

Sodium: 131mg

Potassium: 576mg

Carbohydrates: 15g

Protein: 11g

Sweet Potato Toast Three Ways

Preparation time: 15 minutes

Cooking time:2 5 minutes

Servings:

Ingredients:

- 1 large sweet potato, unpeeled

- Topping Choice #1:

- 4 tablespoons peanut butter

- 1 ripe banana, sliced

- Dash ground cinnamon

- Topping Choice #2:

- ½ avocado, peeled, pitted, and mashed

- 2 eggs (1 per slice)

- Topping Choice #3:

- 4 tablespoons nonfat or low-fat ricotta cheese

- 1 tomato, sliced

- Dash black pepper

Directions:

1. Slice the sweet potato lengthwise into ¼-inch thick slices. Place the sweet potato slices in a toaster on high for about 5 minutes or until cooked through.

2. Repeat multiple times, if necessary, depending on your toaster settings. Top with your desired topping choices and enjoy.

Nutrition:

Calories: 137

Fat: 0g

Sodium: 17mg

Potassium: 265mg

Carbohydrates: 32g

Fiber: 4g

Sugars: 0g

Protein: 2g

Apple-Apricot Brown Rice Breakfast Porridge

Preparation time: 15 minutes

Cooking time: 8 minutes

Servings: 4

Ingredients:

- 3 cups cooked brown rice

- 1¾ cups nonfat or low-fat milk

- 2 tablespoons lightly packed brown sugar

- 4 dried apricots, chopped

- 1 medium apple, cored and diced

- ¾ teaspoon ground cinnamon

- ¾ teaspoon vanilla extract

Directions:

1. Combine the rice, milk, sugar, apricots, apple, and cinnamon in a medium saucepan. Boil it on medium heat, lower the heat down slightly and cook within 2 to 3 minutes. Turn it off, then stir in the vanilla extract. Serve warm.

Nutrition:

Calories: 260

Fat: 2g

Sodium: 50mg

Potassium: 421mg

Carbohydrates: 57g

Fiber: 4g

Sugars: 22g

Protein: 7g

Carrot Cake Overnight Oats

Preparation time: overnight

Cooking time: 2 minutes

Servings: 1

Ingredients:

- ½ cup rolled oats

- ½ cup plain nonfat or low-fat Greek yogurt

- ½ cup nonfat or low-fat milk

- ¼ cup shredded carrot

- 2 tablespoons raisins

- ½ teaspoon ground cinnamon

- 1 to 2 tablespoons chopped walnuts (optional)

Directions:

1. Mix all of the fixings in a lidded jar, shake well, and refrigerate overnight. Serve.

Nutrition:

Calories: 331

Fat: 3g

Sodium: 141mg

Carbohydrates: 59g

Fiber: 8g

Sugars: 26g

Protein: 22g

Steel-Cut Oatmeal with Plums and Pear

Preparation time: 15 minutes

Cooking time: 25 minutes

Servings: 4

Ingredients:

- 2 cups of water

- 1 cup nonfat or low-fat milk

- 1 cup steel-cut oats

- 1 cup dried plums, chopped

- 1 medium pear, cored, and skin removed, diced

- 4 tablespoons almonds, roughly chopped

Directions:

1. Mix the water, milk, plus oats in a medium pot and bring to a boil over high heat. Reduce the heat and cover. Simmer for about 10 minutes, stirring occasionally.

2. Add the plums and pear, and cover. Simmer for another 10 minutes. Turn off the heat and let stand within 5 minutes until all of the liquid is absorbed. To serve, top each portion with a sprinkling of almonds.

Nutrition:

Calories: 307

Fat: 6g

Sodium: 132mg

Potassium: 640mg

Carbohydrates: 58g

Fiber: 9g

Sugars: 24g

Protein: 9g

French Toast with Applesauce

Preparation time: 5 minutes

Cooking time: 5 minutes

Servings: 6

Ingredients:

- ¼ c. unsweetened applesauce

- ½ c. skim milk

- 2 packets Stevia

- 2 eggs

- 6 slices whole-wheat bread

- 1 tsp. ground cinnamon

Directions:

1. Mix well applesauce, sugar, cinnamon, milk, and eggs in a mixing bowl. Soak the bread into the applesauce mixture until wet. On medium fire, heat a large nonstick skillet.

2. Add soaked bread on one side and another on the other side. Cook in a single layer within 2-3 minutes per side on medium-low fire or until lightly browned. Serve and enjoy.

Nutrition:

Calories: 122.6

Fat:2.6 g

Carbs:18.3 g

Protein:6.5 g

Sugars:14.8 g

Sodium: 11mg

Banana-Peanut Butter and Greens Smoothie

Preparation time: 5 minutes

Cooking time: 0 minutes

Servings: 1

Ingredients:

- 1 c. chopped and packed Romaine lettuce

- 1 frozen medium banana

- 1 tbsp. all-natural peanut butter

- 1 c. cold almond milk

Directions:

1. In a heavy-duty blender, add all ingredients. Puree until smooth and creamy. Serve and enjoy.

Nutrition:

Calories: 349.3

Fat:9.7 g

Carbs:57.4 g

Protein:8.1 g

Sugars:4.3 g

Sodium:18 mg

Baking Powder Biscuits

Preparation time: 5 minutes

Cooking time: 5 minutes

Servings: 1

Ingredients:

- 1 egg white

- 1 c. white whole-wheat flour

- 4 tbsps. Non-hydrogenated vegetable shortening

- 1 tbsp. sugar

- 2/3 c. low-Fat milk

- 1 c. unbleached all-purpose flour

- 4 tsp.

- Sodium-free baking powder

Directions:

1. Warm oven to 450°F. Put the flour, sugar, plus baking powder into a mixing bowl and mix. Split the shortening into the batter using your fingers until it resembles coarse crumbs. Put the egg white plus milk and stir to combine.

2. Put the dough out onto a lightly floured surface and knead 1 minute. Roll dough to ¾ inch thickness and

cut into 12 rounds. Place rounds on the baking sheet. Bake 10 minutes, then remove the baking sheet and place biscuits on a wire rack to cool.

Nutrition:

Calories: 118

Fat:4 g

Carbs:16 g

Protein:3 g

Sugars:0.2 g

Sodium: 6 mg

Oatmeal Banana Pancakes with Walnuts

Preparation time: 15 minutes

Cooking time: 5 minutes

Servings: 8

Ingredients:

- 1 finely diced firm banana

- 1 c. whole wheat pancake mix

- 1/8 c. chopped walnuts

- ¼ c. old-fashioned oats

Directions:

1. Make the pancake mix, as stated in the directions on the package. Add walnuts, oats, and chopped banana. Coat a griddle with cooking spray. Add about ¼ cup of the pancake batter onto the griddle when hot.

2. Turn pancake over when bubbles form on top. Cook until golden brown. Serve immediately.

Nutrition:

Calories: 155

Fat:4 g

Carbs:28 g

Protein:7 g

Sugars:2.2 g

Sodium:16 mg

Creamy Oats, Greens & Blueberry Smoothie

Preparation time: 4 minutes

Cooking time: 0 minutes

Servings: 1

Ingredients:

- 1 c. cold

- Fat-free milk

- 1 c. salad greens

- ½ c. fresh frozen blueberries

- ½ c. frozen cooked oatmeal

- 1 tbsp. sunflower seeds

Directions:

1. Blend all ingredients using a powerful blender until smooth and creamy. Serve and enjoy.

Nutrition:

Calories: 280

Fat:6.8 g

Carbs:44.0 g

Protein:14.0 g

Sugars:32 g

Sodium:141 mg

Banana & Cinnamon Oatmeal

Preparation time: 5 minutes

Cooking time: 0 minutes

Servings: 6

Ingredients:

- 2 c. quick-cooking oats

- 4 c. Fat-free milk

- 1 tsp. ground cinnamon

- 2 chopped large ripe banana

- 4 tsp. Brown sugar

- Extra ground cinnamon

Directions:

1. Place milk in a skillet and bring to boil. Add oats and cook over medium heat until thickened, for two to four minutes.

2. Stir intermittently. Add cinnamon, brown sugar, and banana and stir to combine. If you want, serve with the extra cinnamon and milk.   Enjoy!

Nutrition:

Calories: 215

Fat:2 g

Carbs:42 g

Protein:10 g

Sugars:1 g

Sodium:40 mg

Bagels Made Healthy

Preparation time: 5 minutes

Cooking time: 40 minutes

Servings: 8

Ingredients:

- 1 ½ c. warm water

- 1 ¼ c. bread flour

- 2 tbsps. Honey

- 2 c. whole wheat flour

- 2 tsp. Yeast

- 1 ½ tbsps. Olive oil

- 1 tbsp. vinegar

Directions:

1. In a bread machine, mix all ingredients, and then process on dough cycle. Once done, create 8 pieces shaped like a flattened ball. Create a donut shape using your thumb to make a hole at the center of each ball.

2. Place donut-shaped dough on a greased baking sheet then covers and let it rise about ½ hour. Prepare about 2 inches of water to boil in a large pan.

3. In boiling water, drop one at a time the bagels and boil for 1 minute, then turn them once. Remove them and return to the baking sheet and bake at 3500F for about 20 to 25 minutes until golden brown.

Nutrition:

Calories: 228

Fat:3.7 g

Carbs:41.8 g

Protein:6.9 g

Sugars:0 g

Sodium:15 mg

Cereal with Cranberry-Orange Twist

Preparation time: 5 minutes

Cooking time: 0 minutes

Servings: 1

Ingredients:

- ½ c. water

- ½ c. orange juice

- 1/3 c. oat bran

- ¼ c. dried cranberries

- Sugar

- Milk

Directions:

1. In a bowl, combine all ingredients. For about 2 minutes, microwave the bowl, then serve with sugar and milk. Enjoy!

Nutrition:

Calories: 220

Fat:2.4 g

Carbs:43.5 g

Protein:6.2 g

Sugars:8 g

Sodium:1 mg

No Cook Overnight Oats

Preparation time: 5 minutes

Cooking time: 0 minutes

Servings: 1

Ingredients:

- 1 ½ c. low-fat milk

- 5 whole almond pieces

- 1 tsp. chia seeds

- 2 tbsps. Oats

- 1 tsp. sunflower seeds

- 1 tbsp. Craisins

Directions:

1. In a jar or mason bottle with a cap, mix all ingredients. Refrigerate overnight. Enjoy for breakfast.

Nutrition:

Calories: 271

Fat:9.8 g

Carbs:35.4 g

Protein:16.7 g

Sugars:9

Sodium:103 mg

Avocado Cup with Egg

Preparation time: 5 minutes

Cooking time: 0 minutes

Servings: 4

Ingredients:

- 4 tsp. parmesan cheese

- 1 chopped stalk scallion

- 4 dashes pepper

- 4 dashes paprika

- 2 ripe avocados

- 4 medium eggs

Directions:

2. Preheat oven to 375 0F. Slice avocadoes in half and discard the seed. Slice the rounded portions of the avocado to make it level and sit well on a baking sheet.

3. Place avocadoes on a baking sheet and crack one egg in each hole of the avocado. Season each egg evenly with pepper and paprika. Bake within 25 minutes or until eggs is cooked to your liking. Serve with a sprinkle of parmesan.

Nutrition:

Calories: 206

Fat:15.4 g

Carbs:11.3 g

Protein:8.5 g

Sugars:0.4 g

Sodium:21 mg

Mediterranean Toast

Preparation time: 10 minutes

Cooking time: 0 minutes

Servings: 2

Ingredients:

- 1 ½ tsp. reduced-Fat crumbled feta

- 3 sliced Greek olives

- ¼ mashed avocado

- 1 slice good whole wheat bread

- 1 tbsp. roasted red pepper hummus

- 3 sliced cherry tomatoes

- 1 sliced hardboiled egg

Directions:

1. First, toast the bread and top it with ¼ mashed avocado and 1 tablespoon hummus. Add the cherry tomatoes, olives, hardboiled egg, and feta. To taste, season with salt and pepper.

Nutrition:

Calories: 333.7

Fat:17 g

Carbs:33.3 g

Protein:16.3 g

Sugars:1 g

Sodium:19 mg

Instant Banana Oatmeal

Preparation time: 1 minute

Cooking time: 2 minutes

Servings: 1

Ingredients:

- 1 mashed ripe banana

- ½ c. water

- ½ c. quick oats

Directions:

1. Measure the oats and water into a microwave-safe bowl and stir to combine. Place bowl in microwave and heat on high for 2 minutes. Remove the bowl, then stir in the mashed banana and serve.

Nutrition:

Calories: 243

Fat:3 g

Carbs:50 g

Protein:6 g

Sugars:20 g

Sodium:30 mg

Almond Butter-Banana Smoothie

Preparation time: 5 minutes

Cooking time: 0 minutes

Servings: 1

Ingredients:

- 1 tbsp. Almond butter

- ½ c. ice cubes

- ½ c. packed spinach

- 1 peeled and a frozen medium banana

- 1 c. Fat-free milk

Directions:

1. Blend all the listed fixing above in a powerful blender until smooth and creamy. Serve and enjoy.

Nutrition:

Calories: 293

Fat:9.8 g

Carbs:42.5 g

Protein:13.5 g

Sugars:12 g

Sodium:40 mg

Brown Sugar Cinnamon Oatmeal

Preparation time: 1 minute

Cooking time: 3 minutes

Servings: 4

Ingredients:

- ½ tsp. ground cinnamon

- 1 ½ tsp pure vanilla extract

- ¼ c. light brown sugar

- 2 c. low- Fat milk

- 1 1/3 c. quick oats

Directions:

1. Put the milk plus vanilla into a medium saucepan and boil over medium-high heat.

2. Lower the heat to medium once it boils. Mix in oats, brown sugar, plus cinnamon, and cook, stirring2–3 minutes. Serve immediately.

Nutrition:

Calories: 208

Fat:3 g

Carbs:38 g

Protein:8 g

Sugars:15 g

Sodium:33 mg

Buckwheat Pancakes with Vanilla Almond Milk

Preparation time: 10 minutes

Cooking time: 10 minutes

Servings: 1

Ingredients:

- ½ c. unsweetened vanilla almond milk

- 2-4 packets natural sweetener

- 1/8 tsp salt

- ½ cup buckwheat flour

- ½ tsp. double-acting baking powder

Directions:

1. Prepare a nonstick pancake griddle and spray with the cooking spray, place over medium heat. Whisk the buckwheat flour, salt, baking powder, and stevia in a small bowl and stir in the almond milk after.

2. Onto the pan, scoop a large spoonful of batter, cook until bubbles no longer pop on the surface and the entire surface looks dry and (2-4 minutes). Flip and cook for another 2-4 minutes. Repeat with all the remaining batter.

Nutrition:

Calories: 240

Fat:4.5 g

Carbs:2 g

Protein:11 g

Sugars:17 g

Sodium:38 mg

Salmon and Egg Scramble

Preparation time: 15 minutes

Cooking time: 4 minutes

Servings: 4

Ingredients:

- 1 teaspoon of olive oil

- 3 organic whole eggs

- 3 tablespoons of water

- 1 minced garlic

- 6 Oz. Smoked salmon, sliced

- 2 avocados, sliced

- Black pepper to taste

- 1 green onion, chopped

Directions:

1. Warm-up olive oil in a large skillet and sauté onion in it. Take a medium bowl and whisk eggs in it, add water and make a scramble with the help of a fork. Add to the skillet the smoked salmon along with garlic and black pepper.

2. Stir for about 4 minutes until all ingredients get fluffy. At this stage, add the egg mixture. Once the

eggs get firm, serve on a plate with a garnish of avocados.

Nutrition:

Calories: 120

Carbs: 3g

Fat: 4g

Protein: 19g

Sodium: 898 mg

Potassium: 129mg

Pumpkin Muffins

Preparation time: 15 minutes

Cooking time: 20 minutes

Servings: 4

Ingredients:

- 4 cups of almond flour

- 2 cups of pumpkin, cooked and pureed

- 2 large whole organic eggs

- 3 teaspoons of baking powder

- 2 teaspoons of ground cinnamon

- 1/2 cup raw honey

- 4 teaspoons almond butter

Directions:

1. Preheat the oven at 400-degree F. Line the muffin paper on the muffin tray. Mix almond flour, pumpkin puree, eggs, baking powder, cinnamon, almond butter, and honey in a large bowl.

2. Put the prepared batter into a muffin tray and bake within 20 minutes. Once golden-brown, serve, and enjoy.

Nutrition:

Calories: 136

Carbs: 22g

Fat: 5g

Protein: 2g

Sodium: 11 mg

Potassium: 699 mg

Sweet Berries Pancake

Preparation time: 15 minutes

Cooking time: 15 minutes

Servings: 4

Ingredients:

- 4 cups of almond flour

- Pinch of sea salt

- 2 organic eggs

- 4 teaspoons of walnut oil

- 1 cup of strawberries, mashed

- 1 cup of blueberries, mashed

- 1 teaspoon baking powder

- Honey for topping, optional

Directions:

1. Take a bowl and add almond flour, baking powder, and sea salt. Take another bowl and add eggs, walnut oil, strawberries, and blueberries mash. Combine ingredients of both bowls.

2. Heat a bit of walnut oil in a cooking pan and pour the spoonful mixture to make pancakes. Once the bubble comes on the top, flip the pancake to cook

from the other side. Once done, serve with the glaze of honey on top.

Nutrition:

Calories: 161

Carbs: 23g

Fat: 6g

Protein: 3g

Cholesterol: 82 mg

Sodium: 91 mg

Potassium: 252mg

Zucchini Pancakes

Preparation time: 15 minutes

Cooking time: 10 minutes

Servings: 4

Ingredients:

- 4 large zucchinis

- 4 green onions, diced

- 1/3 cup of milk

- 1 organic egg

- Sea Salt, just a pinch

- Black pepper, grated

- 2 tablespoons of olive oil

Directions:

1. First, wash the zucchinis and grate it with a cheese grater. Mix the egg and add in the grated zucchinis and milk in a large bowl. Warm oil in a skillet and sauté onions in it.

2. Put the egg batter into the skillet and make pancakes. Once cooked from both sides. Serve by sprinkling salt and pepper on top.

Nutrition:

Calories: 70

Carbs: 8g

Fat: 3g

Protein: 2g

Cholesterol: 43 mg

Sodium: 60 mg

Potassium: 914mg

Breakfast Banana Split

Preparation time: 15 minutes

Cooking time: 0 minutes

Servings: 3

Ingredients:

- 2 bananas, peeled

- 1 cup oats, cooked

- 1/2 cup low-fat strawberry yogurt

- 1/3 teaspoon honey, optional

- 1/2 cup pineapple, chunks

Directions:

1. Peel the bananas and cut lengthwise. Place half of the banana in each separate bowl. Spoon strawberry yogurt on top and pour cooked oats with pineapple chunks on each banana. Serve immediately with a glaze of honey of liked.

Nutrition:

Calories: 145

Carbs: 18g

Fat: 7g

Protein: 3g

Sodium:2 mg

Potassium: 380 mg

Easy Veggie Muffins

Preparation time: 10 minutes

Cooking time: 40 minutes

Servings: 4

Ingredients:

- ¾ cup cheddar cheese, shredded

- 1 cup green onion, chopped

- 1 cup tomatoes, chopped

- 1 cup broccoli, chopped

- 2 cups non-fat milk

- 1 cup biscuit mix

- 4 eggs

- Cooking spray

- 1 teaspoon Italian seasoning

- A pinch of black pepper

Directions:

1. Grease a muffin tray with cooking spray and divide broccoli, tomatoes, cheese, and onions in each muffin cup.

2. In a bowl, combine green onions with milk, biscuit mix, eggs, pepper, and Italian seasoning, whisk well and pour into the muffin tray as well.

3. Cook the muffins in the oven at 375 degrees F for 40 minutes, divide them between plates, and serve.

Nutrition:

Calories: 80

Carbs: 3g

Fat: 5g

Protein: 7g

Sodium: 25 mg

Carrot Muffins

Preparation time: 10 minutes

Cooking time: 30 minutes

Servings: 5

Ingredients:

- 1 and ½ cups whole wheat flour

- ½ cup stevia

- 1 teaspoon baking powder

- ½ teaspoon cinnamon powder

- ½ teaspoon baking soda

- ¼ cup natural apple juice

- ¼ cup olive oil

- 1 egg

- 1 cup fresh cranberries

- 2 carrots, grated

- 2 teaspoons ginger, grated

- ¼ cup pecans, chopped

- Cooking spray

Directions:

1. Mix the flour with the stevia, baking powder, cinnamon, and baking soda in a large bowl. Add apple juice, oil, egg, cranberries, carrots, ginger, and pecans and stir well.

2. Oiled a muffin tray with cooking spray, divide the muffin mix, put in the oven, and cook at 375 degrees F within 30 minutes. Divide the muffins between plates and serve for breakfast.

Nutrition:

Calories: 34

Carbs: 6g

Fat: 1g

Protein: 0g

Sodium: 52 mg

Pineapple Oatmeal

Preparation time: 10 minutes

Cooking time: 25 minutes

Servings: 4

Ingredients:

- 2 cups old-fashioned oats

- 1 cup walnuts, chopped

- 2 cups pineapple, cubed

- 1 tablespoon ginger, grated

- 2 cups non-fat milk

- 2 eggs

- 2 tablespoons stevia

- 2 teaspoons vanilla extract

Directions:

1. In a bowl, combine the oats with the pineapple, walnuts, and ginger, stir and divide into 4 ramekins. Mix the milk with the eggs, stevia, and vanilla in a bowl and pour over the oats mix. Bake at 400 degrees F within 25 minutes. 4. Serve for breakfast.

Nutrition:

Calories: 200

Carbs: 40g

Fat: 1g

Protein: 3g

Sodium: 275 mg

Spinach Muffins

Preparation time: 10 minutes

Cooking time: 30 minutes

Servings: 6

Ingredients:

- 6 eggs

- ½ cup non-fat milk

- 1 cup low-fat cheese, crumbled

- 4 ounces spinach

- ½ cup roasted red pepper, chopped

- 2 ounces prosciutto, chopped

- Cooking spray

Directions:

1. Mix the eggs with the milk, cheese, spinach, red pepper, and prosciutto in a bowl. Grease a muffin tray with cooking spray, divide the muffin mix, introduce in the oven, and bake at 350 degrees F within 30 minutes. Divide between plates and serve for breakfast.

Nutrition:

Calories: 112

Carbs: 19g

Fat: 3g

Protein: 2g

Sodium: 274 mg

Chia Seeds Breakfast Mix

Preparation time: 8 hours

Cooking time: 0 minutes

Servings: 4

Ingredients:

- 2 cups old-fashioned oats

- 4 tablespoons chia seeds

- 4 tablespoons coconut sugar

- 3 cups of coconut milk

- 1 teaspoon lemon zest, grated

- 1 cup blueberries

Directions:

1. In a bowl, combine the oats with chia seeds, sugar, milk, lemon zest, and blueberries, stir, divide into cups and keep in the fridge for 8 hours. 2. Serve for breakfast.

Nutrition:

Calories: 69

Carbs: 0g

Fat: 5g

Protein: 3g

Sodium: 0 mg

Breakfast Fruits Bowls

Preparation time: 10 minutes

Cooking time: 0 minutes

Servings: 2

Ingredients:

- 1 cup mango, chopped

- 1 banana, sliced

- 1 cup pineapple, chopped

- 1 cup almond milk

Directions:

1. Mix the mango with the banana, pineapple, and almond milk in a bowl, stir, divide into smaller bowls, and serve.

Nutrition:

Calories: 10

Carbs: 0g

Fat: 1g

Protein: 0g

Sodium: 0mg

Pumpkin Cookies

Preparation time: 10 minutes

Cooking time: 25 minutes

Servings: 6

Ingredients:

- 2 cups whole wheat flour

- 1 cup old-fashioned oats

- 1 teaspoon baking soda

- 1 teaspoon pumpkin pie spice

- 15 ounces pumpkin puree

- 1 cup coconut oil, melted

- 1 cup of coconut sugar

- 1 egg

- ½ cup pepitas, roasted

- ½ cup cherries, dried

Directions:

1. Mix the flour the oats, baking soda, pumpkin spice, pumpkin puree, oil, sugar, egg, pepitas, and cherries in a bowl, stir well, shape medium cookies out of this mix, arrange them all on a baking sheet, then bake

within 25 minutes at 350 degrees F. Serve the cookies for breakfast.

Nutrition:

Calories: 150

Carbs: 24g

Fat: 8g

Protein: 1g

Sodium: 220 mg

Veggie Scramble

Preparation time: 10 minutes

Cooking time: 2 minutes

Servings: 1

Ingredients:

- 1 egg

- 1 tablespoon water

- ¼ cup broccoli, chopped

- ¼ cup mushrooms, chopped

- A pinch of black pepper

- 1 tablespoon low-fat mozzarella, shredded

- 1 tablespoon walnuts, chopped

- Cooking spray

Directions:

1. Grease a ramekin with cooking spray, add the egg, water, pepper, mushrooms, and broccoli, and whisk well. Introduce in the microwave and cook for 2 minutes. Add mozzarella and walnuts on top and serve for breakfast.

Nutrition:

Calories: 128

Carbs: 24g

Fat: 0g

Protein: 9g

Sodium: 86 mg

Mushrooms and Turkey Breakfast

Preparation time: 10 minutes

Cooking time: 1 hour and 5 minutes

Servings: 12

Ingredients:

- 8 ounces whole-wheat bread, cubed

- 12 ounces turkey sausage, chopped

- 2 cups fat-free milk

- 5 ounces low-fat cheddar, shredded

- 3 eggs

- ½ cup green onions, chopped

- 1 cup mushrooms, chopped

- ½ teaspoon sweet paprika

- A pinch of black pepper

- 2 tablespoons low-fat parmesan, grated

Directions:

1. Put the bread cubes on a prepared lined baking sheet, bake at 400 degrees F for 8 minutes. Meanwhile, heat a pan over medium-high heat, add turkey sausage, stir, and brown for 7 minutes.

2. In a bowl, combine the milk with the cheddar, eggs, parmesan, black pepper, and paprika and whisk well.

3. Add mushrooms, sausage, bread cubes, and green onions stir, pour into a baking dish, bake at 350 degrees F within 50 minutes. 5. Slice, divide between plates and serve for breakfast.

Nutrition:

Calories: 88

Carbs: 1g

Fat: 9g

Protein: 1g

Sodium: 74 mg

Mushrooms and Cheese Omelet

Preparation time: 10 minutes

Cooking time: 15 minutes

Servings: 4

Ingredients:

- 2 tablespoons olive oil

- A pinch of black pepper

- 3 ounces mushrooms, sliced

- 1 cup baby spinach, chopped

- 3 eggs, whisked

- 2 tablespoons low-fat cheese, grated

- 1 small avocado, peeled, pitted, and cubed

- 1 tablespoons parsley, chopped

Directions:

1. Add mushrooms, stir, cook them for 5 minutes and transfer to a bowl on a heated pan with the oil over medium-high heat.

2. Heat-up the same pan over medium-high heat, add eggs and black pepper, spread into the pan, cook within 7 minutes, and transfer to a plate.

3. Spread mushrooms, spinach, avocado, and cheese on half of the omelet, fold the other half over this mix, sprinkle parsley on top, and serve.

Nutrition:

Calories: 136

Carbs: 5g

Fat: 5g

Protein: 16g

Sodium: 192 mg